THE NUTCRACKER AND THE FOUR REALMS: UNLOCK YOUR DREAMS

A CENTUM BOOK 9781912707669

Published in Great Britain by Centum Books Ltd

This edition published 2018

1 3 5 7 9 10 8 6 4 2

Centum Books Ltd, 20 Devon Square, Newton Abbot, Devon, TQ12 2HR, UK

books@centumbooksltd.co.uk

CENTUM BOOKS Limited Reg. No. 07641486

A CIP catalogue record for this book is available from the British Library

Printed in Poland.

Step into the **FOUR REALMS** with **CLARA,**
PHILLIP and **SUGAR PLUM**

and let their magical wonderland

INSPIRE YOUR IMAGINATION.

Unlock your dreams and let

the adventures come to life…

Search for the **16 KEYS TO THE KINGDOM**
HIDDEN throughout this book.
CLUE: these keys have letters written on them!

On **PAGE 93**, write the letters you've found and
then unscramble them to reveal a secret message.

centum

INVENTING IS MY KIND OF
ADVENTURE

NAME: Clara Stahlbaum ☆

FAVOURITE SUBJECT: Science

LOVES: Inventing, mechanics

TRAITS: Courage, intelligence, wit

MENTOR: Godfather Drosselmeyer

CLARA'S STORY: All Clara wants is to find a **KEY.** Why is it so special and where will her search take her?

Clara is a smart, curious and independent girl who receives a precious gift hidden inside an ornate box. But it's locked and she desperately wants the key to open it. Her search leads her to a strange and mysterious parallel world where her courage, strength and instincts will be tested.

INVENT YOUR OWN WONDER

When Clara wants to catch a mouse, she creates a **GENIUS CONTRAPTION** and her brother, Fritz, is amazed. Put your genius to the test and see what magic you can invent.

What **PROBLEM** would you like to solve?

My missing key

What's your **INVENTION** idea?

Trap little monster

Describe what's **SPECIAL** about it.

Traps MONSTER under bed

NAME your invention here:

Tadpole

List all of the **PARTS** you would need:

* Spoon.
* Wood pice.
* String.
* Big Rook
* not big rocks

BigRock

Spoon

piceWood

Not big
Rocks

INVENTION INSTRUCTIONS:

9

BREAK
→ the ←
COG CODE

Clara's godfather, Drosselmeyer, is working on a **MECHANICAL OWL** – but something has gone wrong. Help Clara fix it by completing the sequences.

BELIEVE

E	L	V	I	B

Unjumble the letter answers to unlock a message from Drosselmeyer.

BELIEVE

10

DECORATE the TREE

Drosselmeyer's **ENORMOUS** Christmas tree is a wonder to behold.

TURN THIS DECORATION INTO SOMETHING EXTRAORDINARY

with perfect patterns and a RAINBOW OF COLOURS.

BEING DIFFERENT IS ALWAYS A
GOOD THING

NAME: Captain Phillip Hoffman

ROLE: Protector of the Four Realms

LOVES: Serving the Kingdom

TRAITS: Brave, loyal, true

HORSE: Jingles

PHILLIP'S STORY: Phillip was once a **TOY NUTCRACKER**, but is now a soldier in the Four Realms. He is the first person to meet Clara when she arrives, and he admires her brilliance and courageous heart.

Phillip is a model captain who is always willing to protect the Four Realms and its people. He admires Clara for her brilliance and courageous heart.

Throughout their adventure, Phillip encourages and supports Clara, never losing faith in her.

INVENT a STORY

Channel your **INNER CLARA** and **TINKER WITH YOUR** *imagination!*

Find your **WORD TOOLS** below and then use them to **BUILD A STORY**.

CIRCLE YOUR FAVOURITE CHARACTER:

TALKING OWL

CLOCKWORK MOUSE

BRAVE SOLDIER

(SKILLED INVENTOR)

UNDERLINE AN OPENING LINE:

~~The enchanted machine heaved into motion.~~

~~THE PALACE SAT HIGH ON THE ROCKS.~~

It was a very special Christmas Eve. *This one!*

~~THE JEWEL WAS SO BRIGHT THAT SHE BLINKED.~~

CHOOSE A STORY TYPE:

(ADVENTUROUS)

SPOOKY

FAIRY TALE

FUTURISTIC

PICK THREE WORDS BELOW THAT MUST APPEAR IN YOUR STORY:

FLEW	GIANT	DISAPPEAR
RACED	CRUEL	SHIMMER
GOLD	RAIN	RECOGNISE
MOON	WINDOW	SURPRISE

TITLE:

A NUTCRACKER NAME

Work out your **ENCHANTED** FOUR REALMS NAME using this guide, then do the same for all your friends.

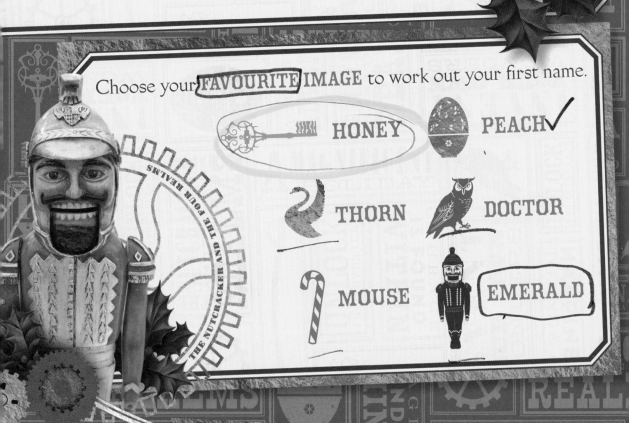

Choose your **FAVOURITE IMAGE** to work out your first name.

HONEY

PEACH ✓

THORN

DOCTOR

MOUSE

EMERALD

Circle a **MIDDLE NAME** of your own choice. *Berry*

BOW

FROST

MY ↘ BIRTH MONTH IS
~~YOUR~~ **TO FIND YOUR LAST NAME.** APRIL!

JANUARY	MOONSHINE	JULY	SPICE
FEBRUARY	FOXGLOVE	AUGUST	CLOUDBALM
MARCH	STARDEER	SEPTEMBER	CLOCKWORK
APRIL	BALLERINA	OCTOBER	WINDMILL
MAY	CAROUSEL	NOVEMBER	WONDERLAND
JUNE	WINGLOVE	DECEMBER	SNOWFALL

CREATE YOUR
NUTCRACKER
SIGNATURE:

★Enchanted

SUGAR AND SPICE
IN A REALM THAT'S SO NICE

NAME: Sugar Plum Fairy

LOVES: ~~Sugar~~ and ~~spice~~

TRAITS: Supreme sweetness

ROLE: Regent of the Land of Sweets

SUGAR PLUM'S STORY: Sugar Plum is a breath of sweet air and this fairy loves telling tales about the magical Four Realms.

Sugar Plum Fairy, beloved regent of the Land of Sweets, wears a gown that sparkles like crystalized sugar. Elegant, ethereal and naturally sweet, Sugar Plum welcomes Clara to the Four Realms with open arms, declaring her the guest of honour at an extravagant pageant.

THE NICE

Tiger

What is as SWEET as
SUGAR PLUM?

FILL IN THE CUPCAKES with your
all-time favourite
FOOD, HOBBIES, BOOKS,
MUSIC and more.

music
Beat it

Books

Food
Hams
+
Eggs

Hobbies
Books

The NOT-SO-SWEET

What things are WORSE than **TOOTHACHE?**

Fill in your *least favourite things* that would be better **LOCKED UP.**

A DREAM
IN EVERY STEP

NAME: Ballerina of the Realms

LOVES: Dancing

TRAITS: Grace, elegance

ROLE: Star performer of the kingdom

BALLERINA'S STORY: This beautiful ballerina is a **SPECIAL STORYTELLER** who shares the enchanted tale of the Realms with Clara through dance.

The Ballerina of the Realms dances with grace and passion at a spectacular pageant created to celebrate Clara's arrival to the Four Realms. The elaborate production reveals to Clara the extraordinary story behind the Land of Snowflakes, Land of Flowers, Land of Sweets and the ominous Fourth Realm.

23

SPARKLING SNOWFLAKES

No two **SNOWFLAKES** are the same
in the **LAND OF SNOWFLAKES**.

Complete the **WINTERY WONDERS** and then fill the pages with **ICY DOODLES.**

PERFECT PACKAGES

Create your own **HOLIDAY** gift wrap
and give your presents a **MAGICAL TOUCH**.

KEY THINGS YOU NEED:

- ROLL OR LARGE SHEETS OF WHITE/BROWN CRAFT PAPER
- COLOURING PENS OR PENCILS
- POSTER PAINT
- STICKERS
- GLITTER
- SCISSORS
- GLUE
- TAPE FOR WRAPPING

WINTER WONDER

❄ Find a POTATO (or other suitable vegetable) and carefully use a knife to cut out a 'Y'-shape – this is a stamp for an arm of a snowflake.

❄ Dip the stamp in paint and then position it to create snowflake shapes across the paper.

❄ Use the end of a pencil dipped in paint to create a polka dot pattern of snow over the rest of the paper.

TIP: USE BROWN PARCEL PAPER SO YOU CAN USE WHITE PAINT FOR THE FLAKES.

ASK AN ADULT TO HELP

BONUS: Draw black lines back and forth across the paper and then dip your fingers in paint. Use your fingerprints to create a string of coloured Christmas lights.

SUPER SWEET

- Draw lots of different sized SPIRALS on the paper.
- Turn some of them into LOLLIPOPS and some into SWEETS and then colour them in.
- Add SPARKLING HIGHLIGHTS with glue and glitter, or get an old toothbrush and dip it in paint. Use your finger to spray the bristles towards the paper and create layers of misty colours.

BONUS: For a sweet treat, attach a candy cane or bag of chocolate coins when you tie your parcel with string.

FLORAL FANCY

- Cut out a large PETAL SHAPE from an old, clean kitchen sponge and stick it to a piece of cardboard.
- Dip your stamp in paint and position petals to create a page full of MULTI-COLOURED FLOWERS.
- Use a mix of STICKERS or the end of a pencil dipped in paint to add spots for the flower centres.

BONUS: Go foraging and tie dried leaves or flowers to your parcel. You can even drop some petals inside.

THAT'S A WRAP!

MORE IDEAS TO TAKE YOUR WRAP TO A HIGHER REALM:

- Reuse MAPS, NEWPAPERS, MAGAZINE PAGES, SHEET MUSIC, OLD WALLPAPER or PAGES FROM LAST YEAR'S CALENDAR as quirky and curious wrapping.
- Use STRING or FABRIC SCRAPS as fancy ribbon.
- Add a stylish HANDMADE TAG with a piece of brown card cut into a triangle at one end. Use a hole punch to add a single hole and tie with string.

STRINGS

NAME: Mother Ginger

ROLE: Regent of the Fourth Realm

TRAITS: Calculating and cunning

HELPERS: Mice and Polichinelles

MOTHER GINGER'S STORY: The Realms were once a place of peace, but Mother Ginger changed everything when she tried to take control.

Regent of the eerie and misty Fourth Realm, **MOTHER GINGER** is a villain bent on destruction. With the help of her mice and a group of acrobatic Polichinelles, she frightens the whole kingdom.

She controls a gigantic porcelain marionette with a hoop skirt that resembles a circus tent. Could Clara's music box key be hidden in Mother Ginger's lair?

MAKE A PERFECT
POLICHINELLE

CLOWN AROUND with **MOTHER GINGER'S** ACROBATIC HELPERS! Create an **OUT-OF-THE-ORDINARY CHARACTER** that's ready to **FLIP** off the page.

GIVE ~~HIM~~ HER A CLOWN-DERFUL NAME:

Soë

~~DESCRIBE YOUR CHARACTER:~~

it has a ponytale~~l~~

WHAT IS THEIR ACROBATIC SKILL?

PICK SOME CLOTHES AND ACCESSORIES:

- ☒ HAT WITH BELL
- ☑ POM-POMS
- ☒ BRACES
- ☒ FRILLY SHIRT
- ☒ WAISTCOAT
- ☒ STRIPY SHORTS
- ☑ POINTY HAT
- ☒ GLOVES
- ☒ CHECKED SOCKS
- ☒ STAR BELT BUCKLE
- ☒ COG BUTTONS
- ☒ BAGGY TROUSERS

WHICH FABRIC PATTERN SUITS YOUR CLOWN?

DRAW YOUR OWN
POLICHINELLE

with all of its WONDERS and CURIOSITIES.

COBWEB OF DREAMS

During a COBWEB PARTY at Drosselmeyer's mansion, CLARA finds a TAG with her name on it and *follows the golden thread all the way to the Four Realms.*

Add your name here:
_____

FOLLOW THIS THREAD and for every tag, fill in one of your WILDEST WISHES.

FOLLOW YOUR DREAMS.

33

WHAT'S your REALM?

In which enchanted land could you be **REGENT**?
Follow the questions to find where you would fit in the **FOUR REALMS**.

Me

SUGARY LAND OF TREATS is for you. Pick a **GINGERBREAD HOUSE** and enjoy the **CANDY-CANE TREES** and **CHOCOLATE-COVERED EARTH**.

Sadie

The best thing about **WINTER** is the **SNOW GAMES** and the endless sparkling of snow and ice. Settle in to the Land of Snowflakes.

START

SWIMMING OR ICE SKATING?

SWIMMING

ICE SKATING

SWEET OR SAVOURY?

SWEET

SAVOURY

MORNING

MORNING OR NIGHTTIME?

NIGHT

CHRISTMAS OR BIRTHDAY?

BIRTHDAY

PLAY OUTSIDE OR INSIDE?

OUTSIDE

INSIDE

The LAND OF FLOWERS

Sadie

You fit perfectly in the **RAINBOW-COLOURED LAND OF FLOWERS**. The houses, fields and even the people are decorated with **BLOSSOMS** – it's a floral paradise.

SWANS OR OWLS?

SWANS

OWLS

me

The 4th REALM

BALLERINA OR SOLDIER?

BALLERINA

SOLDIER

PARK OR FOREST?

PARK

FOREST

CHRISTMAS

The **MYSTERIOUS**, misty **FOURTH REALM** is full of **AMUSEMENTS** – and maybe there's more than what you see.

PICNIC OR SNOWBALL FIGHT?

PICNIC

SNOWBALL FIGHT

DISCOVER *a new* REALM

What if **CLARA** were to discover **ANOTHER REALM?**
Design an imaginary **'FIFTH REALM'** that would bring
a whole new world of play for the **NUTCRACKER** characters.

THE NEW LAND IS CALLED:
THE LAND OF MAGIC

WHAT IS UNUSUAL ABOUT THE LAND?
there is Fariys and UNICORNS!

WHY WOULD PEOPLE WANT TO VISIT?
cause it is.....um fun
and magical!

WHAT DO THE BUILDINGS LOOK LIKE?
they are made of chocolate!

WHAT ANIMALS LIVE THERE?
unicoras and narwhals and
fox Angels!

WONDERS *of* SCIENCE

CLARA loves SCIENCE AND MECHANICS and she uses her knowledge to create **BRILLIANT INVENTIONS**. Experiment with these simple demos at home and see what wonders you can create.

SWEET-STYLE SPIRALS

TRY THIS CANDY-INSPIRED COLOUR DEMONSTRATION.

What you'll need:

- FLAT BAKING TRAY
- FOOD COLOURING IN 3 COLOURS OR MORE
- LIQUID DISH SOAP
- FULL-FAT MILK

WHAT TO DO:

1. Carefully pour some milk into the tray so that it covers the bottom.
2. Add 8 drops of food colouring (in a variety of colours) into the milk in different spots.
3. Add 5 drops of soap around the drops of food colouring and see what happens...

FLORAL FANCY

CREATE YOUR OWN MAGICAL BLOOMS FIT FOR THE LAND OF FLOWERS.

What you'll need:

- WHITE CARNATION FLOWERS
- SMALL VASE OR GLASS
- FOOD COLOURING IN 1 OR 2 COLOURS
- SCISSORS

WHAT TO DO:

1. Pick a food colouring – this will be the colour added to your flower.
2. Pour some water into the glass and add several drops of food colouring until it is a deep colour.
3. Snip the end of the carnation stem and put the flower in the coloured water.
4. Wait for the next day or two and see what happens to the petals...

MULTI-COLOURED BONUS:

Ask an adult to split the bottom of the stem with scissors. Place each side of the stem into a different glass with different coloured water.

CRYSTAL TOWER

CHILL OUT WITH AN ICY EXPERIMENT THAT HAS A HOT TWIST.

What you'll need:

❄ **750ML OF WHITE VINEGAR**

❄ **4 TABLESPOONS OF BAKING SODA**

❄ **MEDIUM-SIZED POT**

❄ **GLASS JUG OR MASON JAR**

❄ **GLASS DISH OR PLATE**

WHAT TO DO:

1. Pour the vinegar into a pot. Add the baking soda one tablespoon at a time and stir until the mixture stops fizzing.

2. Heat the mixture over a low–medium heat for up to one hour until the liquid reduces by around three quarters. White powdery crystals should start to form on the sides of the pot.

3. Put the mixture in a glass jug and place in the fridge to cool for 30-45 minutes.

4. Scrape a little of the dried crystal powder from the inside of the pot and place it in the centre of the glass dish.

5. Carefully remove the chilled liquid solution from the fridge – don't bump it! Slowly pour it over the crystals on the dish and see what happens…

ICY BONUS: Melt the mixture in a pot again to repeat and create a new sculpture. You can add a drop of leftover food colouring and see if it will make coloured crystals!

39

CURIOUS CROSSWORD

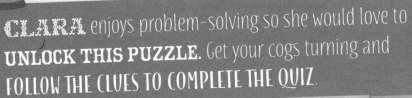

CLARA enjoys problem-solving so she would love to **UNLOCK THIS PUZZLE.** Get your cogs turning and **FOLLOW THE CLUES TO COMPLETE THE QUIZ.**

ACROSS

2. The name of CLARA'S GODFATHER (12)
5. The GIANT MOUSE MONSTER is called the Mouse **king** (4)
8. The name of PHILLIP'S BRAVE HORSE (7) **Jingles**
11. Clara follows a golden **thread** to the FOUR REALMS (6)
12. What is Clara's SURNAME? (9)
13. What COLOUR is Clara's party dress? (6)
15. The Polichinelles are the HELPERS of Mother **ginger** (6)

DOWN

1. What OBJECT is Clara searching for? (3)
3. Name this SUPREMELY SWEET CHARACTER (5,4)
4. CLARA'S ADVENTURES BEGIN on Christmas **eve** (3)
6. The name of CLARA'S BROTHER (5)
7. What kind of DANCER tells the story of the Realms? (9)
9. The LAND FULL OF CANDY is called the Land of **sweets** (6)
10. What is the SEASON in the Land of Snowflakes? (6)
14. CLARA'S MOTHER gifts her an ornate locked **egg** (3)

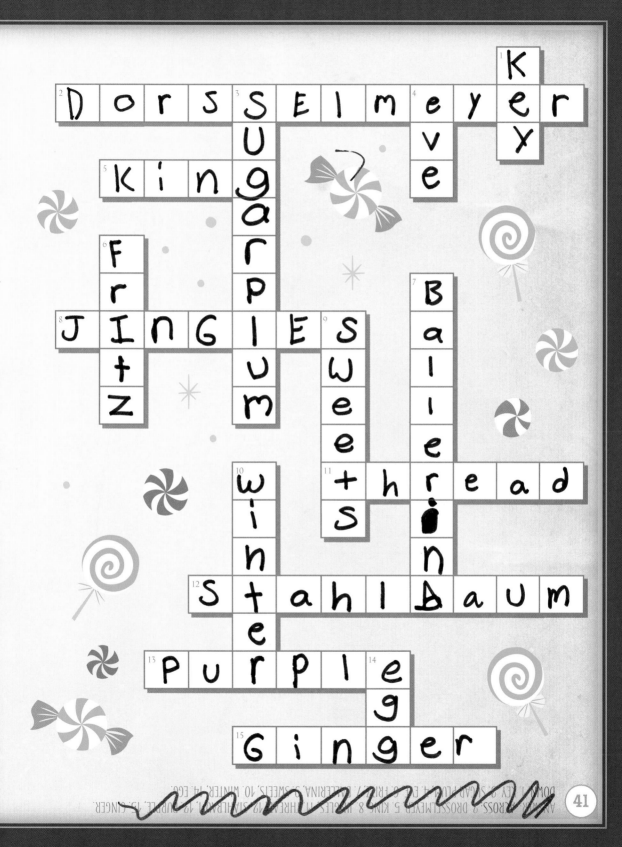

The crossword puzzle contains the following answers:

Across:
2. DORSSELMEYER
5. KING
8. JINGLES
11. THREAD
12. STAHLBAUM
13. PURPLE
15. GINGER

Down:
1. KEY
3. SUGARPLUM
4. EVE
6. FRITZ
7. BALLERINA
9. SWEETS
10. WINTER
14. EGO

CLOCK OF MEMORIES

DROSSELMEYER'S GRANDFATHER CLOCK

is no ORDINARY CLOCK.

Use the enchanted clock faces to peek back at 12 of your favourite memories. NOTE THE TREASURES WITHIN.

1

2

3

4

AN ADVENTURE TO REMEMBER.

VINTAGE LETTERS

Try this FUN CRAFT *to create your own* VINTAGE LETTERS.

OLD NOTES

with handwritten messages

HOLD A SPECIAL KIND OF

MAGIC.

WHAT YOU'LL NEED:

* Sheets of plain white paper
* Paintbrush
* Cup of warm coffee
* Hairdryer

WHAT TO DO:

1. Use the paintbrush to PAINT a layer of COFFEE over your paper.

2. Use the HAIRDRYER to DRY the paper, then turn it over and do the same on the other side.

3. Keep PAINTING and DRYING more layers until you have the colour you want.

4. Include some SCORE MARKS with the other end of your paintbrush and rub the edges of the paper while it's wet to give it a more aged look. Then finish with your final layer of coffee and dry.

5. FOLD, CRUMPLE and SMOOTH sections of the sheet as you like. Now your vintage paper is ready!

INVENTION TIPS:

✳ Use the **SAME STEPS** to **AGE** your ENVELOPES so you have *vintage pockets* to ADDRESS YOUR NOTES.

✳ Roll your letter up and tie it with string to create a **SCROLL.** These make perfect **THEMED INVITES!**

Copy this style of writing to give your letters supreme script style!

To my beautiful Clara,
Everything you need
is inside.

Love,
Mother

WHAT WOULD BOOST YOUR CONFIDENCE?
Write some secret inspirational notes for yourself.

to one! um...
i don't know what
to say...
Nothing!

CRACK the QUIZ

How well do you know the land of SUGAR PLUM and **MOTHER GINGER?** Test your NUTCRACKER know-how with this **FUN TRIVIA QUIZ.**

1

WHAT IS CLARA'S FAVOURITE HOBBY?

A DRESSING UP

B INVENTING

C GROOMING HORSES

2

WHAT COLOUR DOES SWEET SUGAR PLUM WEAR?

A WHITE & RED

B PINK & PURPLE

C PURPLE & GOLD

3

WHO IS THE FIRST PERSON CLARA MEETS IN THE FOUR REALMS?

A PHILLIP

B SUGAR PLUM

C REGENT OF THE LAND OF FLOWERS

4

WHAT ARE THE TREES MADE OF IN THE LAND OF SWEETS?

A SNOW

B CHOCOLATE BARS

C CANDY CANES

5 WHAT IS MOTHER GINGER'S REALM KNOWN AS?

A FOURTH REALM

B LAND OF FLOWERS

C WONDERLAND

6 WHAT KIND OF ANIMALS ARE MOTHER GINGER'S HELPERS?

A HORSES

B OWLS

C MICE

7 WHO PRESENTS THE DANCE AT CLARA'S SPECIAL PAGEANT?

A SUGAR PLUM

B BALLERINA OF THE REALMS

C REGENT OF THE LAND OF SNOWFLAKES

8 WHO BROUGHT ALL THE TOYS OF THE REALM TO LIFE?

A CLARA

B DROSSELMEYER

C CLARA'S MOTHER

9 WHAT IS THE NAME OF THE CLOWN-LIKE ACROBATS WHO FLIP AND DIVE ALL OVER?

A RINKMASTERS

B POLICHINELLES

C FERRIS CLOWNS

Now, count up the answers that you got right.

1-3 CORRECT: NUTCRACKER NEWBIE

4-6 CORRECT: SUGAR PLUM SUPER

7-9 CORRECT: FOUR REALMS FANTASTIC!

ANSWERS: 1.b, 2.b, 3.a, 4.c, 5.a, 6.c, 7.b, 8.c, 9.b.

WONDROUS TALES

Imagination is the key to invention — but how strong are your story skills?

Try these GAMES with FRIENDS and FAMILY to see how quickly you can SPIN NEW TALES.

INVENT YOUR OWN — WONDERS — THE NUTCRACKER AND THE FOUR REALMS

THE LAST LETTER

YOU NEED A GROUP OF PEOPLE FOR THIS GAME. Sit in a circle and prepare to tell a story with only one sentence per person. Choose someone to go first and they should say their sentence aloud. Then each player must begin their sentence with the last letter of the last word of the previous player's sentence. NO PAUSING!

AWESOME TO AWFUL

ONE PERSON SHOULD START TELLING A STORY – it can be about something real or it can be an imaginary tale set in the Four Realms. The story should start in a positive way, focusing on only good things that have happened. Then, another player makes a buzzer sound. On that sound, the storyteller should bring only bad and negative things into the story. Each time the buzzer sounds, the story should shift from 'awesome' to 'awful' – with the buzzer getting quicker as the game goes on!

CURIOUS OBJECTS

Test your on-the-spot storytelling with this quick-fire game that you can play with two people or more. One person should close their eyes while another chooses a random object in the room.

As soon as the first person opens their eyes they should start telling a magical story about that object. It can be as silly as you like, but you must not stop speaking for 30 seconds.

DO YOU SPEAK GIBBERISH?

Can you CLOWN AROUND like a **POLICHINELLE?**

How about a story game where you don't use words at all? In this game, it's not about what you say but how you say it.

Come up with characters, a scene and an idea for what is happening. Now act it out – but the only dialogue you can use is silly made-up words and sounds. See how well you can understand each other!

NUTCRACKER SURPRISE

Each player should write a name, character type or object from the Nutcracker on a slip of paper. Some examples you can use are: **MOUSE, KEY, MOTHER GINGER, TOY SOLDIER, BALLET DANCER.** Put the paper slips in a hat.

Two players should begin an improvised scene. Once they get going, they should take it in turns to pick out a word and add it to their dialogue. Whatever the word says, keep the scene going!

COURAGE SAVES THE DAY

CLARA and **PHILLIP** have to face their FEARS on their journey through the Realms. List your **BIGGEST FEARS** and then the times when you've found courage and faced them head-on.

I'm SUPER SCARED of...

* _____
* _____
* _____
* _____
* _____
* _____
* _____
* _____
* _____
* _____
* _____
* _____

My PROUDEST **BRAVE MOMENTS** are…

DOODLE IT UP

Get set for some
DRAWING INVENTIONS.

Create OBJECTS or CHARACTERS
fit for **THE REALMS** from these SHAPES
by doodling them into something new.

UNLOCK THE
EXTRAORDINARY.

A CHARACTER OF WONDERS

You've met many of the COLOURFUL CHARACTERS who live in this MAGICAL LAND — who else do you imagine might live there? Create a BRAND NEW CHARACTER to join the adventure.

The character is a:

◯ **HUMAN**   ◯ **ANIMAL**   ☑ **FAIRY**

◯ **SOLDIER**   ◯ **OTHER** _____

If it's an animal, WHICH ANIMAL IS IT? _____

The character is best friends with:

The character lives in:

Fill in the profile for your character:

Name: _____

Loves: _____

Traits: _____

Helpers: _____

Role: _____

Character's story: _____

DRAW YOUR NEW CHARACTER HERE.

ALIVE FOR
ADVENTURE.

SHORT AND SWEET

Write a SHORT STORY that features your **NEW CHARACTER** and what unfolds when they meet **CLARA** in the Realms.

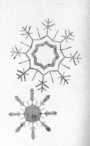

Find the
MAGIC
in your
mind.

FIND YOUR *friendship style*

CLARA and **PHILLIP** are the best of friends and share lots of traits. WHAT KIND OF FRIEND ARE YOU? Find out in this BRILLIANT QUIZ.

ARE YOU THE **LEADER** IN YOUR GROUP OF FRIENDS?

YES

NO

ARE YOU THE 'FUNNY ONE' WITH YOUR FRIENDS?

DO YOUR FRIENDS SHARE **SECRETS** WITH YOU?

NO

YES

NO

YES

DO YOU HAVE MORE THAN ONE **BEST FRIEND?**

DO YOU AND YOUR FRIENDS SHARE **SECRET NOTES?**

HAVE YOU DONE SOMETHING TO **HELP A FRIEND** THIS WEEK?

YES

NO

NO

NO

YES

YES

WOULD YOUR FRIENDS SAY YOU'RE **SENSITIVE?**

WOULD YOUR FRIENDS DESCRIBE YOU AS **LOUD?**

WOULD YOU BE **BEST FRIENDS** WITH CLARA?

NO

YES

NO

YES

NO

YES

SWEET *and a* **GOOD LISTENER**

A

FUN AND INVENTIVE

BOLD AND LOYAL

61

WONDERS of FRIENDSHIP

Name: **Wren**

Known for: **4** years

Favourite thing about them: **Likes Horses**

Talent:drawing

Best moment together: _____

Best quote: _____

_____

Name: _____

Known for: _____ years

Favourite thing about them: _____

Talents: _____

Best moment together: _____

Best quote: _____

_____

Name: _____

Known for: _____ years

Favourite thing about them: _____

Talents: _____

Best moment together: _____

Best quote: _____

_____

Name: _____

Known for: _____ years

Favourite thing about them: _____

Talents: _____

Best moment together: _____

Best quote: _____

_____

THE SEARCH GOES ON

Clara's search isn't just for the **KEY** – it's a journey inside, too.
Help **CLARA** on her search by FINDING
THE NUTCRACKER WORDS in the grid.

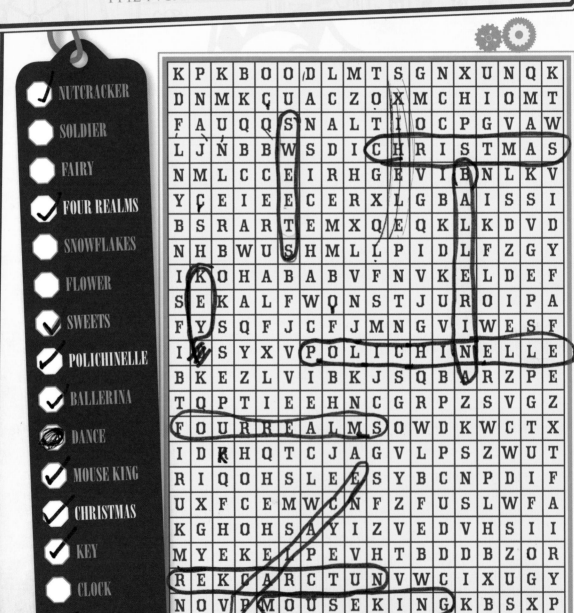

- ✓ NUTCRACKER
- SOLDIER
- FAIRY
- ✓ FOUR REALMS
- SNOWFLAKES
- FLOWER
- ✓ SWEETS
- ✓ POLICHINELLE
- ✓ BALLERINA
- DANCE
- ✓ MOUSE KING
- ✓ CHRISTMAS
- ✓ KEY
- CLOCK
- ✓ PALACE

Answer on page 65

Nutcracker

ISN'T IT CURIOUS?

The best way to FIND ANSWERS is to ASK QUESTIONS – just like **CLARA** does with Drosselmeyer. What WONDROUS and CURIOUS questions have you always wanted to ask? *List them below.*

GIFT LIST

There are few FEELINGS more **MAGICAL** than **GIVING GIFTS TO OTHERS.** *Keep a list of gift ideas here so that you're always prepared.*

Gift for: Present ideas:

_____ _____

_____ _____

_____ _____

_____ _____

_____ _____

_____ _____

_____ _____

_____ _____

_____ _____

_____ _____

_____ _____

_____ _____

A thoughtful gift that you've made yourself is extra sweet.

Create your own

GIFT WRAP

- SEE PAGE 26.

Gift for:

Present ideas:

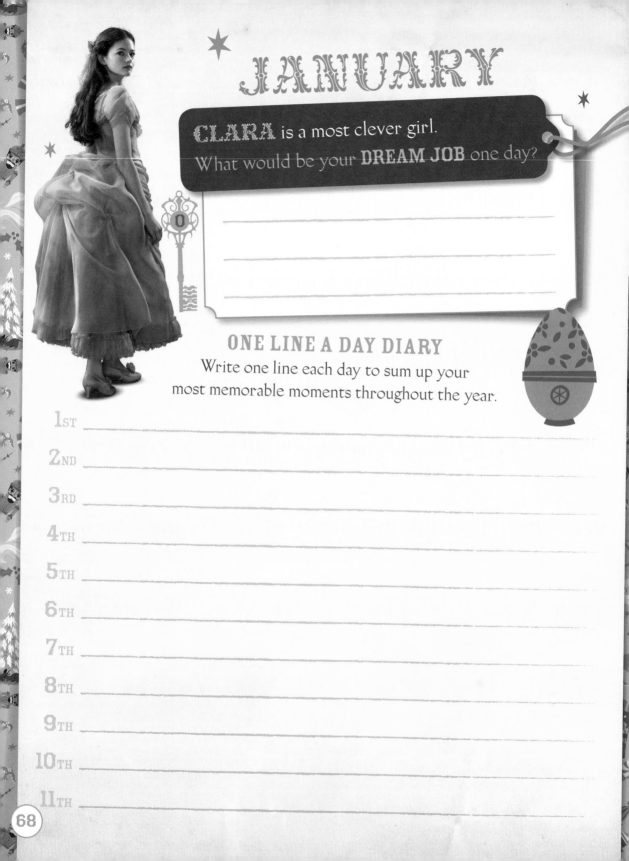

JANUARY

CLARA is a most clever girl.
What would be your **DREAM JOB** one day?

_____
_____
_____

ONE LINE A DAY DIARY

Write one line each day to sum up your
most memorable moments throughout the year.

1ST _____
2ND _____
3RD _____
4TH _____
5TH _____
6TH _____
7TH _____
8TH _____
9TH _____
10TH _____
11TH _____

12TH _____

13TH _____

14TH _____

15TH _____

16TH _____

17TH _____

18TH _____

19TH _____

20TH _____

21ST _____

22ND _____

23RD _____

24TH _____

25TH _____

26TH _____

27TH _____

28TH _____

29TH _____

30TH _____

31ST _____

FEBRUARY

1ST _____

2ND _____

3RD _____

4TH _____

5TH _____

6TH _____

7TH _____

8TH _____

9TH _____

10TH _____

11TH _____

12TH _____

13TH _____

14TH _____

15TH _____

16TH _____

17TH _____

18TH _____

19TH _____

EVERY DAY brings **NEW WONDERS.**
Give someone a **NICE SURPRISE** this month.

The
4th
REALM

Doodle a STAR here when it's done.

20TH

21ST

22ND

23RD

24TH

25TH

26TH

27TH

28TH

71

MARCH

WHAT are you DAYDREAMING about

THIS MONTH?

_____

_____

_____

_____

1ST _____

2ND _____

3RD _____

4TH _____

5TH _____

6TH _____

7TH _____

8TH _____

9TH _____

10TH _____

11TH _____

12TH _____

13TH _____

14TH _____

15TH _____

16TH _____

17TH _____

18TH _____

19TH _____

20TH _____

21ST _____

22ND _____

23RD _____

24TH _____

25TH _____

26TH _____

27TH _____

28TH _____

29TH _____

30TH _____

31ST _____

APRIL

1st ~~MY BIRTHDAY~~

2nd

3rd _my birthday!

4th

5th

6th

7th

8th

9th

10th

11th

12th

13th

14th

15th

16th

17th

18th

19th

Sugar Plum thinks
sweetness rules.
What do you ADMIRE MOST
in someone?

HONESTY ☑

HUMOUR ⬡

INTELLIGENCE ⬡

Kindness ☑
OTHER

20th _____

21st _____

22nd _____

23rd _____

24th _____

25th _____

26th _____

27th _____

28th _____

29th _____

30th _____

MAY

CURIOUS THINKERS discover **MAGIC**.

Write down the **BEST FACT** you learn this month.

1ST

2ND

3RD

4TH

5TH

6TH

7TH

8TH

9TH

10TH

11TH

12TH _____

13TH _____

14TH _____

15TH _____

16TH _____

17TH _____

18TH _____

19TH _____

20TH _____

21ST _____

22ND _____

23RD _____

24TH _____

25TH _____

26TH _____

27TH _____

28TH _____

29TH _____

30TH _____

31ST _____

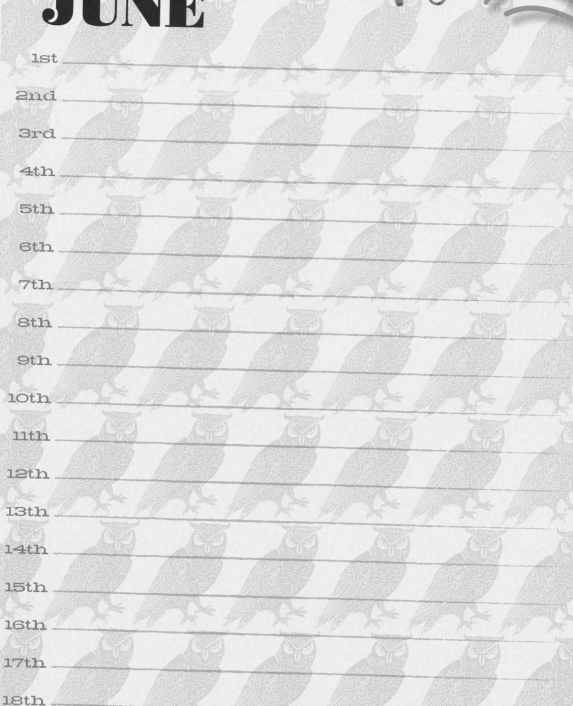

JUNE

1st _____

2nd _____

3rd _____

4th _____

5th _____

6th _____

7th _____

8th _____

9th _____

10th _____

11th _____

12th _____

13th _____

14th _____

15th _____

16th _____

17th _____

18th _____

19th _____

ALWAYS FOLLOW YOUR DREAMS.

What ONE THING would you

LOVE TO ACHIEVE this month?

20th _____

21st _____

22nd _____

23rd _____

24th _____

25th _____

26th _____

27th _____

28th _____

29th _____

30th _____

JULY

This month is ALIVE with **ADVENTURE.**

WHAT NEW THING WILL YOU TRY?

Draw a **SNOWFLAKE** here when it's done.

1ST _____

2ND _____

3RD _____

4TH _____

5TH _____

6TH _____

7TH _____

8TH _____

9TH _____

10TH _____

11TH _____

12TH _____

13TH _____

14TH _____

15TH _____

16TH _____

17TH _____

18TH _____

19TH _____

20TH _____

21ST _____

22ND _____

23RD _____

24TH _____

25TH _____

26TH _____

27TH _____

28TH _____

29TH _____

30TH _____

31ST _____

AUGUST

1ST _____

2ND _____

3RD _____

4TH _____

5TH _____

6TH _____

7TH _____

8TH _____

9TH _____

10TH _____

11TH _____

12TH _____

13TH _____

14TH _____

15TH _____

16TH _____

17TH _____

18TH _____

19TH _____

COURAGE is found WITHIN.
What **FEAR** will you face this month?

COURAGE
IS FOUND WITHIN
THE NUTCRACKER AND THE FOUR REALMS

20TH

21ST

22ND

23RD

24TH

25TH

26TH

27TH

28TH

29TH

30TH

31ST

SEPTEMBER

Be an **INDEPENDENT THINKER.**
What's your **FAVOURITE THING** to do on your own?

DOODLE IT HERE.

1ST _____

2ND _____

3RD _____

4TH _____

5TH _____

6TH _____

7TH _____

8TH _____

9TH _____

10TH _____

11TH _____

12TH _____

13TH _____

14TH _____

15TH _____

16TH _____

17TH _____

18TH _____

19TH _____

20TH _____

21ST _____

22ND _____

23RD _____

24TH _____

25TH _____

26TH _____

27TH _____

28TH _____

29TH _____

30TH _____

OCTOBER

1ST _____

2ND _____

3RD _____

4TH _____

5TH _____

6TH _____

7TH _____

8TH _____

9TH _____

10TH _____

11TH _____

12TH _____

13TH _____

14TH _____

15TH _____

16TH _____

17TH _____

18TH _____

19TH _____

The best **GIFT** is the gift of ADVENTURE.
Think of a **NEW GAME** for your friends.
Describe it here:

20TH _____
21ST _____
22ND _____
23RD _____
24TH _____
25TH _____
26TH _____
27TH _____
28TH _____
29TH _____
30TH _____
31ST _____

NOVEMBER

Unlock the **EXTRAORDINARY** inside you.

Name one **UNUSUAL TALENT** you'd love to learn.

1ST

2ND

3RD

4TH

5TH

6TH

7TH

8TH

9TH

10TH

11TH

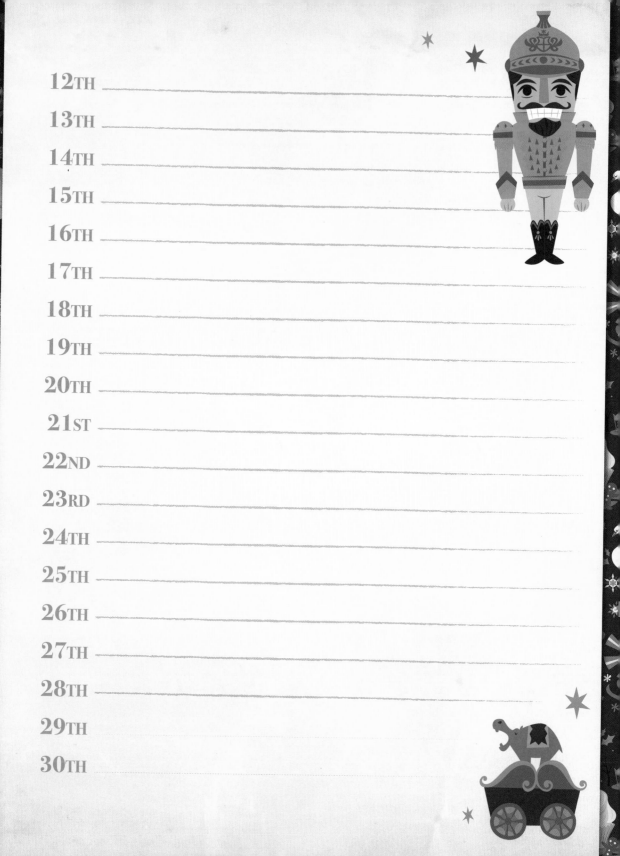

12TH ....

13TH ....

14TH ....

15TH ....

16TH ....

17TH ....

18TH ....

19TH ....

20TH ....

21ST ....

22ND ....

23RD ....

24TH ....

25TH ....

26TH ....

27TH ....

28TH ....

29TH ....

30TH ....

DECEMBER

1ST ....

2ND ....

3RD ....

4TH ....

5TH ....

6TH ....

7TH ....

8TH ....

9TH ....

10TH ....

11TH ....

12TH ....

13TH ....

14TH ....

15TH ....

16TH ....

17TH ....

18TH ....

19TH ....

Open the **MAGIC** of the season.

WHAT WOULD YOU LIKE FOR CHRISTMAS?

1 _____

2 _____

3 _____

20TH _____

21ST _____

22ND _____

23RD _____

24TH _____

25TH _____

26TH _____

27TH _____

28TH _____

29TH _____

30TH _____

31ST _____

HAVE YOU FOUND

the keys

TO THE KINGDOM?

Did you spot ALL OF THE

HIDDEN KEYS

in the book?

It's time to unlock the message they hold.

Write all of the **KEY LETTERS** here, and then USE THE SPACE BELOW to

UNSCRAMBLE THE MESSAGE.

 A PAGE 9
 E PAGE 16
 D PAGE 21
 W PAGE 23
 R PAGE 27
 S PAGE 29
 V PAGE 32
 N PAGE 42

 E PAGE 51
 A PAGE 52
 R PAGE 57
 O PAGE 61
 E PAGE 67
 T PAGE 68
 F PAGE 76
T PAGE 83

adventures   begin   with
wonder

The **SECRET MESSAGE** of the keys is:

ANSWER: Adventures begin with wonder.